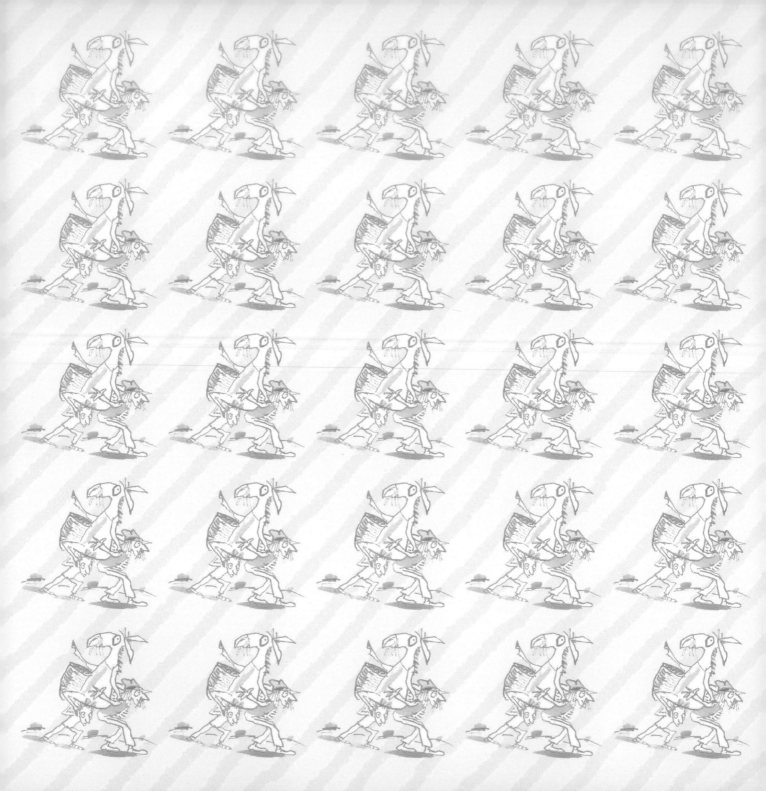

This book belongs to ...

....

OXFORD

UNIVERSITY PRESS

Great Clarendon Street, Oxford, OX2 6DP, United Kingdom

Oxford University Press is a department of the University of Oxford.
It furthers the University's objective of excellence in research, scholarship and
education by publishing worldwide. Oxford is a registered trade mark of Oxford
University Press in the UK and in certain other countries

The Foolish Fox, Three Rocks Text © Oxford University Press 2011
Tom, Dad and Colin Text © Jan Burchett and Sara Vogler 2011
Hans in Luck Text © Paeony Lewis 2011
Tom, Dad and Colin Illustrations © Tony Ross 2011
The Foolish Fox Illustrations © Matte Stephens 2011
Three Rocks Illustrations © Mark Beech 2011
Hans in Luck Illustrations © Andrés Martínez Ricci 2011

The moral rights of the author have been asserted

The Foolish Fox, Three Rocks, Hans in Luck, Tom, Dad and Colin first published in 2011

This Edition published in 2013

British Library Cataloguing in Publication Data
Data available

ISBN: 978-0-19-273606-2

10 9 8 7 6 5 4 3 2 1

Typeset in OUP Earlybird

Printed in China

Paper used in the production of this book is a natural, recyclable product
made from wood grown in sustainable forests. The manufacturing process
conforms to the environmental regulations of the country of origin.

Acknowledgements

Series Advisor: Nikki Gamble

Help your child's learning
with essential tips, phonics
support and free eBooks
www.oxfordowl.co.uk

Oxford
Reading
Tree

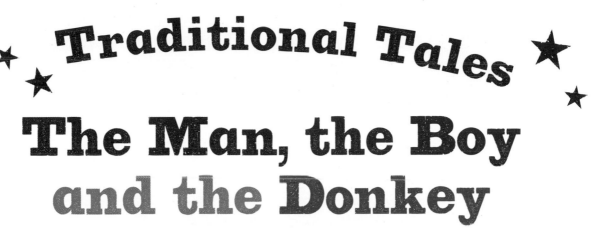

Traditional Tales

The Man, the Boy and the Donkey

and Other Stories

OXFORD
UNIVERSITY PRESS

Tips for reading Tom, Dad and Colin together

About the story

This story is a simple retelling of Aesop's fable 'The Man, the Boy and the Donkey'.

This book practises blending adjacent consonants in words, e.g. the two sounds 'p' and 'l' in 'plod'.

pl fr spl cl
nd st nch nt

Ask your child to find these letter combinations in the story and read the words.

Your child might find these words tricky:

said have so were little when

Say these words for your child if they do not know them.

- Before you begin, ask your child to read the title to you by sounding out and blending. Talk about what the story might be about. Which name do you think belongs to each character?

- Encourage your child to read the story to you. Talk about the pictures as you read.

- Your child will be able to read most of the words in the story, but if they struggle with a word, remind them to say the sounds in the word from left to right. Ask them to point to the sounds as they say them, and then blend the sounds into a whole word, e.g. c-l-o-p.

- After you have read the story look through it again and talk about it. Why did they try to carry the donkey? Was it a good idea to try and please everyone?

- Do the 'Retell the story' activity together!

Watch this story being performed by a professional storyteller on www.oxfordowl.co.uk

Tom, Dad and Colin

Written by Jan Burchett and Sara Vogler

Illustrated by Tony Ross

OXFORD
UNIVERSITY PRESS

Tom set off for town, with his dad on Colin's back.

Little Town 8

Plod, plod, plod went Tom's feet down the long, hard road.

Little Town 7

A man went up to Dad.
"Let him get on," he said.

So Dad got down from Colin's back.
Tom got on Colin.

Plod, plod, plod went Dad's feet down the long, hard road.

Little Town 5

A man ran up to Tom.
"Let him get on too," he said.

Little Town 4

So Dad got on Colin.

Clop, clop, clop went
Colin's feet down
the long, hard road.

Little Town 3

A man sat on a bench.
"Let him have a rest," he said
to Tom and Dad.

Little Town 2

So they got down from Colin's back. Colin got on Tom and Dad.

Plod, plod, plod they went down the long, hard road to town.

Little Town 1

When they got to town,
lots of children were
looking at them.

Little
Town

Tom and Dad felt foolish.

Tom and Dad did
not see the pond.

Splash!

They all fell in.

Tom and Dad were fed up.
Now they were wet...

...and so was Colin!

Retell the story

Encourage your child to retell the story in their own words using the pictures as prompts. You could do this together, or take it in turns. Have fun!

Once upon a time...

The end.

Tips for reading The Foolish Fox together

This story is a simple retelling of a traditional tale from Argentina.

This book practises blending adjacent consonants in words, e.g. the two sounds 'x' and 't' in 'next'.

xt nd st cr tr

Ask your child to find these letter combinations in the story and read the words.

Your child might find these words tricky:

said like so some were when

Say these words for your child if they do not know them.

- Before you begin, ask your child to read the title to you by sounding out and blending. Talk about what the story might be about. What might the fox be like? Can you think of some foxes from other stories? What are they like? (sly, clever)

- Encourage your child to read the story to you. Talk about the pictures as you read.

- Your child will be able to read most of the words in the story, but if they struggle with a word, remind them to say the sounds in the word from left to right. Ask them to point to the sounds as they say them, and then blend the sounds into a whole word, e.g. f-ar-m.

- After you have read the story look through it again and talk about what happened. Who do you think was most clever? Fox or the sheep? Why?

- Do the 'Retell the story' activity together!

The Foolish Fox

Written by Alison Hawes

Illustrated by Matte Stephens

OXFORD
UNIVERSITY PRESS

Fox

Sheep

Fox had a farm but he
did not like farming.

So he said to some sheep, "Farm my land for me, and you can keep some of the food."

The sheep said, "Can we keep the *top* part of the food or the *bottom* part?" "The top part," said Fox.

29

So the sheep put corn seeds in the soil.

When the corn was high,
the sheep cut it down.

Then they took the corn
roots to Fox.

"This is not food!" said Fox.
Fox was cross. It had been a trick!

Fox said, "Next year, you must keep the *bottom* part of the food."

So the sheep put turnip seeds in the soil.

35

When the turnips were big,
the sheep dug them up.

They took the turnip tops to Fox.

"This is not food!" said Fox.
Fox was cross. It had been a trick!

So now, Fox farms his land himself!

Encourage your child to retell the story in their own words using the pictures as prompts. You could do this together, or take it in turns. Have fun!

Once upon a time...

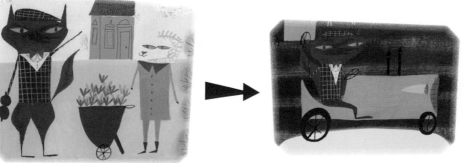

The end.

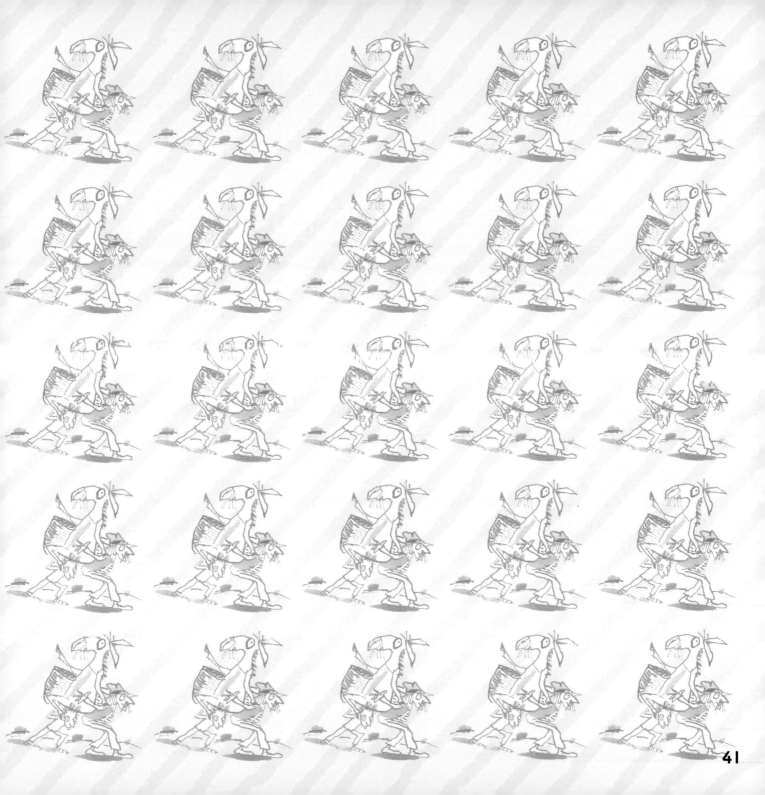

Tips for reading Three Rocks together

This story is a simple retelling of the story 'Stone Soup', also known as 'Axe Soup' and 'Nail Soup' in some parts of Europe.

This book practises blending adjacent consonants in words, e.g. the two sounds 's' and 't' in 'roast' or 'stuck'.

thr br st
sm nt

Ask your child to find these letter combinations in the story and read the words.

Your child might find these words tricky:

said have so some one out

Say these words for your child if they do not know them.

- Before you begin, ask your child to read the title to you by sounding out and blending. Talk about what the story might be about.

- Encourage your child to read the story to you. Talk about the pictures as you read.

- Your child will be able to read most of the words in the story, but if they struggle with a word, remind them to say the sounds in the word from left to right. Ask them to point to the sounds as they say them, and then blend the sounds into a whole word, e.g. b-r-ow-n.

- After you have read the story look through it again and talk about what happened. What did the man put in the pot? Did he play an unkind trick?

- Do the 'Retell the story' activity together!

Three Rocks

Written by Monica Hughes

Illustrated by Mark Beech

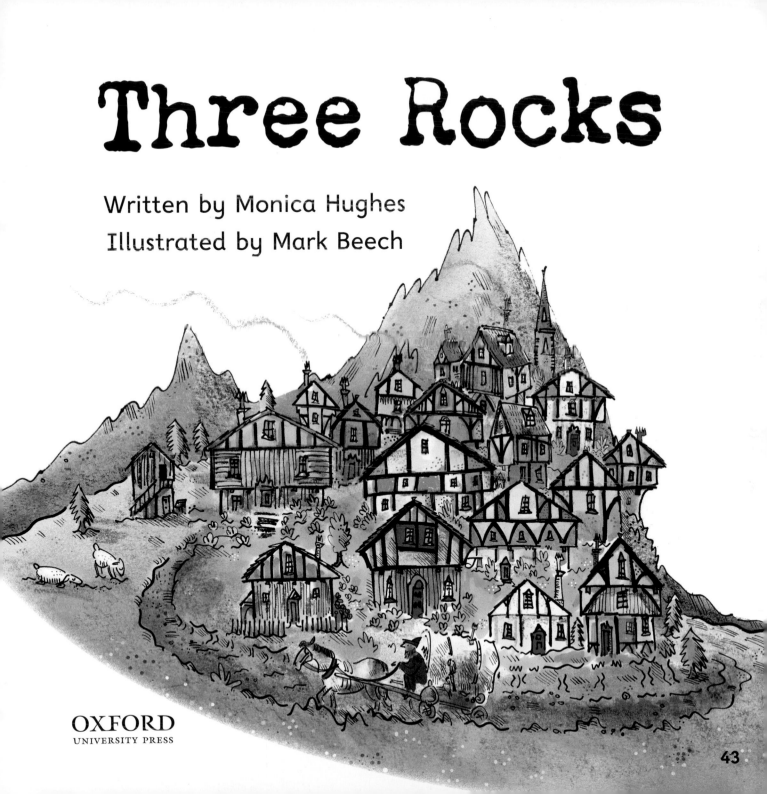

One winter, a man went
to a little town.

"We have no food for you. Shoo, get out of town," they all said.

Get rid of him!

"I can cook dinner for you,"
said the man.

He got a big pot.
Into the pot he put three big rocks.

"It smells good, but it will be better with brown stock," the man said.

So into the pot he put brown stock with the three big rocks.

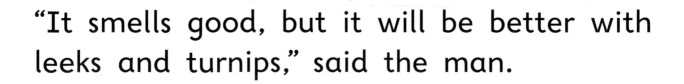

"It smells good, but it will be better with leeks and turnips," said the man.

So into the pot he put the leeks and
the turnips, with the brown stock
and the three big rocks.

"It smells good, but it will be better
with some roast chicken," he said.

54

So into the pot he put the roast chicken, with the leeks and the turnips, the brown stock and the three big rocks.

"This *is* good!" they all said.

The children said, "But *you* all
put the food into the pot!"

Encourage your child to retell the story in their own words using the pictures as prompts. You could do this together, or take it in turns. Have fun!

Once upon a time...

The end.

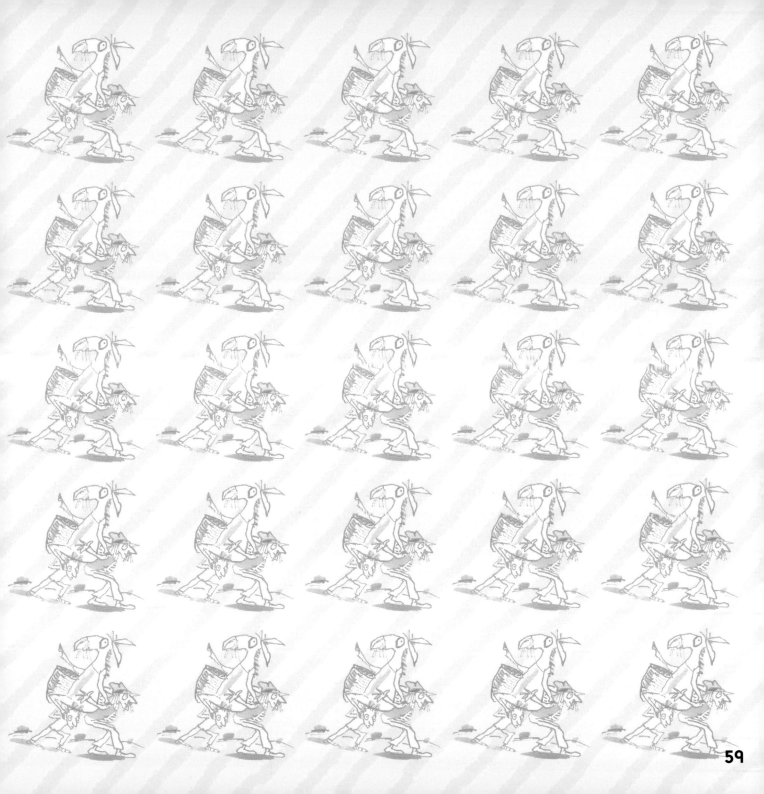

Tips for reading Hans in Luck together

This story is a simple retelling of the German tale 'Hans in Luck', which was written down by the Brothers Grimm over 200 years ago.

This book practises blending adjacent consonants in words, e.g. the two sounds 'l' and 'k' in 'milk'.

lk nd

Ask your child to find these letter combinations in the story and read the words.

Your child might find these words tricky:

said   have   like   so   there little   out   what   some

Say these words for your child if they do not know them.

- Before you begin, ask your child to read the title to you by sounding out and blending. Talk about what the story might be about.

- Encourage your child to read the story to you. Talk about the pictures as you read.

- Your child will be able to read most of the words in the story, but if they struggle with a word, remind them to say the sounds in the word from left to right. Ask them to point to the sounds as they say them, and then blend the sounds into a whole word, e.g. m-i-l-k.

- After you have read the story look through it again and talk about what Hans did with his silver. Did he get something better each time? Would you have kept the silver?

- Do the 'Retell the story' activity together!

Hans in Luck

Written by Paeony Lewis

Illustrated by Andrés Martínez Ricci

OXFORD
UNIVERSITY PRESS

Long ago, Hans set out
to visit his mum.

It was hot on the road and Hans had a big bag of silver.

"He looks quick," said Hans.

"You can have him for the bag of silver," said the man.

"What luck!" said Hans.

But Hans fell off!

Ow!

There was a farmer with a cow.
"I like milk," said Hans.

"You can have my cow if I can have him," said the farmer. "What luck!" said Hans.

But the cow had no milk.

Sigh...

Hans met a man with a chicken.
He said, "You can have my chicken."
"What luck!" said Hans. "I like eggs."

But Hans got a peck.

Hans met a miller
with a big mill rock
and a little mill rock.

"What luck!" said Hans.
"I will have some buns."

But the rocks fell in a deep pond.

Oops!

With no rocks, Hans was now quick.

So Hans said, "Mum! I had good luck."

Retell the story

Encourage your child to retell the story in their own words using the pictures as prompts. You could do this together, or take it in turns. Have fun!

Once upon a time...

The end.

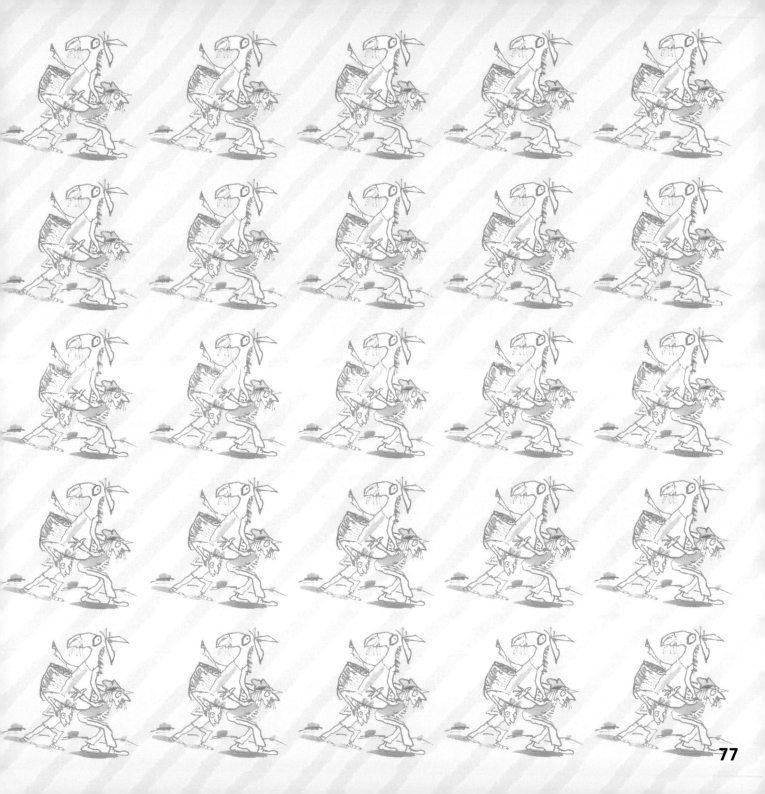

Practise Your Phonics With
★ Traditional Tales ★

More stories for you to enjoy...

Practise Your Phonics With Traditional Tales — Stage 1+
The Gingerbread Man and Other Stories
4 stories you can read by yourself!
OXFORD

Practise Your Phonics With Traditional Tales — Stage 2
The Tortoise and the Hare and Other Stories
4 stories you can read by yourself!
OXFORD

Practise Your Phonics With Traditional Tales — Stage 3
Chicken Licken and Other Stories
4 stories you can read by yourself!
OXFORD

Practise Your Phonics With Traditional Tales — Stage 4
The Man, the Boy and the Donkey and Other Stories
4 stories you can read by yourself!
OXFORD

Coming soon...

Practise Your Phonics With Traditional Tales
Jack and the Beanstalk and Other Stories
4 stories you can read by yourself!
OXFORD

Practise Your Phonics With Traditional Tales — Stage 8
How the Bear Lost His Tail and Other Stories
4 stories you can read by yourself!
OXFORD

Help your child's learning with essential tips, phonics support and free eBooks

www.oxfordowl.co.uk

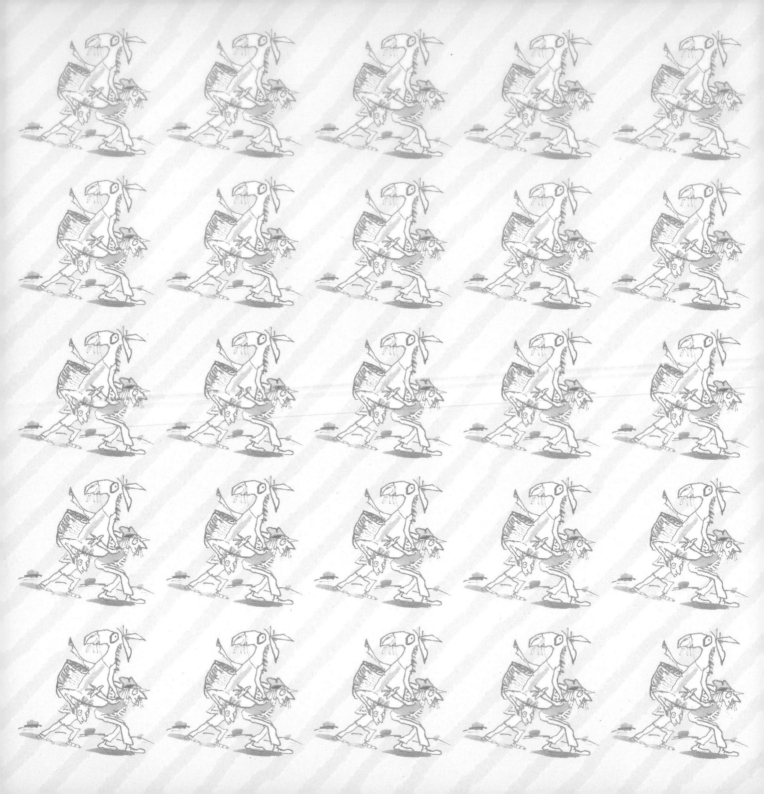